INTEGRATING
PRIMITIVE REFLEXES
THROUGH PLAY AND EXERCISE

AN INTERACTIVE GUIDE TO THE MORO REFLEX FOR PARENTS, TEACHERS, AND SERVICE PROVIDERS

KOKEB GIRMA MCDONALD, OTR/L
OCCUPATIONAL THERAPIST REGISTERED/LICENSED

ISBN: 978-1-7342143-0-7

DEDICATION

MY HUSBAND

Thank you for your love and support. Your dedication to making a positive difference in the world continues to inspire me daily.

PARENTS AND CAREGIVERS

To all parents and caregivers of children with special needs. You take on more than most, and continuously strive to better the future of your children, often without the support you and your children need. I hope this book eases your challenging journey and offers you a useful tool for incorporating helpful exercises in your home. Remember, you are not alone!

TEACHERS

You are one of our children's primary influencers and game-changers. Helping you to create a safe and effective classroom for all children is my main goal. Outside of the home, you have the most impact on our children's development.

FELLOW SERVICE PROVIDERS

Lastly, to my fellow occupational therapists and service providers, you work hard to meet the needs of your students, often not seeing the fruits of your labor. Working alongside you has been a great privilege and is what pushes me to continue finding effective solutions to our client's and their family's needs every day. Together we can make a difference!

YOUR FREE GIFT

Thank you for purchasing my book. As a thank you, I have compiled a mini downloadable social story you can use with a child.

The social story includes challenges a child with a retained Moro reflex may face and coping strategies he or she can use.

Visit socialstory-moro-downloads.polaristherapy.com
to receive your file.

TABLE OF CONTENTS

Introduction   1

Chapter 1: The Benefits of Reflexes   5

Chapter 2   7

    A. What Is the Moro Reflex?   7

    B. Benefits of the Moro Reflex   8

    C. Retained Moro Reflex: Symptoms and Behaviors   9

Chapter 3: Testing and Screening   11

    Table #1: Symptoms and Behavior Checklist—Moro Reflex   11

    The Starfish Exercise Screen   14

Chapter 4   17

    A. Intervention and Treatment Planning   17

    B. Accommodations   17

    C. Exercises to Promote Moro Reflex Integration   18

        1. The Starfish on Beanbag   20

        2. Starfish on Chair   24

        3. Starfish Standing   28

        4. Bridge   32

        5. Splat   35

        6. Duck Walk Holding a Stick   38

        7. Pigeon Walk Holding a Stick   42

        8. Duck Walk Holding a Marker   44

        9. Pigeon Walk Holding a Marker   46

        10. Duck Walk Without Holding Anything   48

11. Pigeon Walk Without Holding Anything 50

12. Duck and Pigeon Hop Holding a Marker 52

13. Duck and Pigeon Hop Without a Marker 55

14. Earth Hugger (Forward) 57

15. Earth Hugger (Backwards) 60

16. Popcorn on Floor 63

17. Popcorn on Therapy Ball 66

18. Hug a Ball 69

19. Hug a Ball: Alternating Arms and Legs 71

20. Hot Potatoes 75

21. Ball Pass Over the Head and Between Legs 78

22. Slither Like Snake on Back 81

23. Balloon Toss 84

24. Growing Tree 88

25. Monkey Bars 91

26. Banana Kicks 94

27. Rocking on Therapy Ball 96

28. Horizontal Bolster Swings 99

29. Diagonal Bolster Swings 101

30. Moon Swing 104

31. Moon Swing and Trapeze 106

Chapter 5: Additional Recommendations and Resources 109

A. How Do You Know If Exercises Are Working? 109

B. Suggested Movement Breaks to Help with Moro
Integration 110

Table #2: Suggested Movement Breaks to Incorporate
throughout the Day 111

C. Treatment Ideas for Occupational Therapists Working
in Clinic Setting 112

    D. Letter to Parent/Caregiver   113

    Table #3: Moro Reflex Integration Exercise Log   115

Glossary   119

Resources   123

About the Author   125

INTRODUCTION

As a working parent, I can testify that it is hard to come home from a busy workday and do therapeutic exercises with one's child. You are tired and your child is fatigued from a hectic day at school. The last thing any parent wants to do is start an activity your child will fight you over. Even as a trained pediatric occupational therapist, I am challenged when I make these home exercises a chore for my child and less motivated to do them when I do not fully understand the reason behind the activities. The best therapeutic programs are those that are fun, playful, and exploratory. The truth is that it takes creativity and professional guidance to set up a successful home program that can be easily carried out.

Children learn through play and repetition, and the best interventions are those that incorporate these activities in the child's natural setting: their home. For a therapeutic team to achieve effective home programs, treatment plans should be a collaboration between parents and therapists. Therapists guide a child's development more effectively if they partner with parents in the treatment planning and execution process. In most cases, a child receives a weekly or bi-weekly one-on-one therapy session with little to no interaction between parents and therapists. While this approach can be helpful, it will not be as effective as a team approach. Like rowing a boat, you will get to your destination faster and with less energy when everyone on the crew works together.

Since parents are their children's first teachers and are the most likely to motivate and influence them, they are well suited to incorporate movement recommendations throughout the week. In this way, they (1) provide needed repetition and (2) easily discern which interventions are working well and can give feedback to the therapist. This integrated process not only helps to achieve faster results, but it also reduces the number of therapy sessions needed—and therefore reduces the total cost incurred by parents. Furthermore, when parent-therapist collaboration is weak, the therapist can only rely on data collected during an individual therapy session in a controlled environment, as opposed to assessing skills that are being practiced in the child's home life. This gap in data may lead to termination of a potentially effective intervention that could have been beneficial.

In this first book of the series, I have compiled simple, step-by-step therapeutic exercises which focus on the Moro reflex, one of the first primitive reflexes. These exercises can be used at home by parents or in the office by trained professionals. If you are a parent, make sure to consult your child's occupational therapist or physician before you begin any intervention program or modify any program given to you by your clinician.

The goal of this handbook is threefold:

1. **Be a resource for service providers.** Provide accessible resources for the specialist working to integrate the Moro reflex. It includes a brief explanation of the Moro reflex, its onset and integration, benefits, and the symptoms that arise when the reflex does not become dormant.

2. **Offer simple, step-by-step therapeutic home exercises.** This handbook includes a menu of simple therapeutic exercises, clear goals, and a progress-tracking guide for a home-based program. It also includes simple explanations for each activity and why these were chosen to address a particular need.

3. **Provide an easy to use parent and teacher training manual.** The best intervention is one that carries over from the therapeutic setting into the home and classroom. By implementing exercises that can be learned easily and quickly, we provide needed repetition and consistency, and, in turn, see results faster. Parents and service providers can work together on the same goal using the tracking charts provided in the appendix.

This program is not intended as medical advice and should be implemented with the help of a trained service provider.

This handbook should not be used to diagnose any condition or disease or replace other therapeutic reflex integration programs.

WHAT ARE PRIMITIVE REFLEXES?

Reflexes are normal, involuntary movement patterns that promote motor learning and sensory integration. Motor learning is a neurological ability to learn new movement skills through practice and repetition. Sensory integration is the mind and body's ability to perceive internal and external information through the senses, learn, respond, and adapt accordingly. Our senses include but not limited to sight, hearing, taste, smell, touch, vestibular (sense of movement and balance), and proprioceptive (body awareness).

Primitive reflexes are involuntary movement patterns that are present at birth and become dormant, or "integrated," before the child reaches 12 months of age. Most reflexes become integrated into a pattern of movement after infancy, so more mature and voluntary movements can emerge. However, sometimes reflexes do not become integrated and interfere with a child's ability to develop an appropriate foundation for stability and mobility. Therefore, a child without integrated primitive reflexes may learn faulty and maladaptive movement patterns (Oden, 2004). Trained therapists can observe these faulty responses by the way a child reacts, behaves, and moves. An effective way to address this interference in reflex integration is to help the child recreate activities a typically developing child would have performed in order to integrate reflexes. Repetition of the therapeutic exercises will give the child a second chance to reintegrate and rewire the brain-body connection.

CHAPTER 1

THE BENEFITS OF REFLEXES

Primitive reflexes are involuntary movement patterns controlled by the brain stem and executed without reaching the cortical or conscious part of the brain. Primitive reflexes emerge in utero, and integrate before the child reaches about 12 months of age. These reflexes include the Moro Reflex, Rooting Reflex, Palmar (Grasp) Reflex, Asymmetrical Tonic Neck Reflex (ATNR), Spinal Galant Reflex, Tonic Labyrinthine Reflex (TLR), and Symmetrical Tonic Neck Reflex (STNR).

Primitive reflexes are necessary during the birthing process, and they are key to the infant's first-year survival. Instinctively, the infant responds to the world via the primitive reflexes. Together the reflexes help the infant move through the birth canal, take his or her first breath, instinctively withdraw from hazardous stimuli, urinate, creep, grasp, lift their heads, open their mouth, suck and swallow, and kick. Each primitive reflex has its benefits and is a building block to the infant's future movement patterns and how he or she perceives the world via the senses. Therefore, primitive reflexes also impact emotional development. In a healthy and typically developing brain, the infant slowly begins to integrate these reflexes naturally, and they become dormant, so a more mature reflex pattern called the "postural reflexes" can develop.

Postural reflexes are mature patterns of responses that control balance, motor coordination, and sensory motor development. Postural reflexes succeed primitive reflexes, and retention of the latter will affect the child's development. It is challenging to work on the child's postural reflexes, for instance, without first going back and making sure the brain has integrated the primitive reflexes. For this reason, therapists should start treatment with primitive reflex screening and integration programs to set a solid developmental foundation.

In cases where there is the presence of trauma, genetic abnormality, chronic illness, developmental delays, or pregnancy or birthing complications, primitive reflexes may still be actively present in the child's body. If primitive reflexes are actively present when they should be inhibited, they are called "retained reflexes." Retained reflexes will continue to cause involuntary movement patterns or physical responses that will in turn cause faulty learning processes. Also, as the baby continues to grow, he or she begins to perceive the world in an immature way, and behavioral challenges may follow.

When a child's brain is healthy and developing typically, maturation and growth are automatic. The child goes through natural and instinctive movement patterns that assist the brain in learning and integrating primitive reflexes. We see confusion in the brain when the child either does not go through the typical milestones or skips them altogether. For example, when a child moves from sitting to walking, skipping the crawling phase, an essential process for brain integration, this jump in development can confuse further development which requires the right and left the brain to coordinate to execute more advanced movement activities.

Every natural developmental stage is essential, and the brain uses each one for critical learning and essential growth. Similarly, a skilled therapist can integrate retained reflexes by following the natural developmental process and mimicking activities and movements that were missed or done incorrectly in the child's previous stages to help the brain rewire itself.

CHAPTER 2

A. WHAT IS THE MORO REFLEX?

The Moro reflex is a primitive reflex pattern that typically emerges in utero and integrates approximately four months after birth. It is an involuntary reaction to what is perceived as an outside threat. The threatening stimuli can come in via touch, sound, or the feeling of being dropped, which creates a sense of falling.

Threatening sensory stimuli includes

- Sudden, loud noises

- Sudden change or movement in the visual field

- The feeling of being dropped or startled

Motor response includes

- Fanning and clenching of fingers

- Spreading or extending the extremities

- Followed by a quick flexion of extremities

- Crying and/or anger

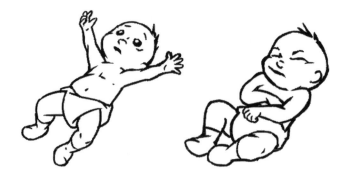

Other physical responses include

- Quick inhalation

- Startling or freezing

- Arousal

- Fight or flight responses

- Sympathetic nervous system activation

  o Increased heart rate, blood pressure, and breathing

  o Adrenaline & cortisol release (stress response)

B. BENEFITS OF THE MORO REFLEX

Moro is the first primitive reflex to emerge, and it is necessary for an infant's survival. Right after birth, the Moro reflex helps the infant take the first breath. It also helps protect the infant from dangerous environmental stimuli by causing physical and behavioral responses that help the child withdraw from a threatening stimulus. The infant pulls away or cries, and, without this primitive reflex, caregivers would not immediately respond to an infant's distress, and provide the necessary comfort. Therefore, it is crucial that we observe the Moro active in an infant's first few months of life. At approximately four months, the Moro reflex will start to integrate and a more mature Startle reflex develops. Instead of relying on the extension and flexion responses of the Moro reflex, the infant will transition to the Startle and Grasp reflex. When this transition is not smooth and the Moro continues to persist, the infant's developmental process will be affected.

C. RETAINED MORO REFLEX: SYMPTOMS AND BEHAVIORS

Moro is the only primitive reflex connected to all other senses, and it is considered a building block to all the other reflexes and overall development. Because the Moro triggers the sympathetic nervous system, it affects the adrenal glands and the production of stress hormones, changing the emotional and physical state of the child. When retained past the necessary time, the Moro puts the body in a constant fight or flight state and causes many adverse symptoms in the body. Also, when the adrenal glands are continuously bombarded with fight or flight signals, they begin to fatigue, and secondary health symptoms, such as reduced immune system and allergies, emerge.

For downloadable version, visit
retained-moro-symptoms.polaristherapy.com.

Signs and symptoms of a retained Moro reflex:

- Sensitivity to sound (auditory defensiveness)

- Poor coordination

- Reduced attention

- Poor balance

- Gravitational insecurities, excessive fear of falling and height

- Motion sickness

- Difficulty tuning out background noise

- Visual perceptual problems

- Increased distractibility

- Easily startled and fearful in new situations

- Overreacting

- Increased "fight or flight" responses or anxiety

- Distractibility

- Hypersensitivity to touch

- Light sensitivity

- Difficulty making decisions

- Difficulty with social skills

- Behavioral and emotional issues

- Low immune system (e.g. allergies, adrenal fatigue, and food sensitivities)

CHAPTER 3

TESTING AND SCREENING

There are specific testing methods that trained therapists and service providers use to check for retained Moro reflex. This book however, is not designed to teach any testing method. To learn more about testing as a teacher, refer to *Assessing Neuromotor Readiness for Learning: INPP Developmental Screening Test and School Intervention Programme.* For trained clinicians, consult *Neuromotor Immaturity in Children and Adults: The INPP Screening Test for Clinicians and Health Practitioners.*

While not a formal evaluation method, I have compiled a symptoms and behavioral checklist (Table #1) to be filled out by parents and teachers in the screening process. This screening list should only be used to gather data and not to diagnose any condition.

TABLE #1 SYMPTOMS AND BEHAVIOR CHECKLIST: MORO REFLEX

Observe the child and circle the number that best represents the severity of the symptoms you observe. You can use this checklist as a screen to gather an initial baseline and then again 6-12 weeks after intervention to assess progress.

Scoring guide: zero being not observed to 5 being observed as severe.

	Symptoms and Behaviors						
1	Hypersensitivity to light	0	1	2	3	4	5
2	Hypersensitivity to sound (e.g. poor auditory discrimination skills, difficulty tuning out noises)	0	1	2	3	4	5
3	Hypersensitivity to touch or sudden touch	0	1	2	3	4	5
4	Hypersensitivity to activities during which a child's feet leave the ground or the head is tilted backward (e.g. avoids swings, somersaults, during bath time to wash hair or even when trying to lay on the back)	0	1	2	3	4	5
5	Motion sickness (e.g. does not like car rides, feels sick easily, and nausea)	0	1	2	3	4	5
6	Overreacts to routine circumstances and events (e.g. may react aggressively and/or strongly)	0	1	2	3	4	5
7	Difficulty calming down, becomes easily distressed (e.g. emotional outbursts, needs extra time to feel safe and calm down)	0	1	2	3	4	5
8	Anxiety	0	1	2	3	4	5
9	Easily distracted by surroundings	0	1	2	3	4	5
10	Impulsive and/or aggressive	0	1	2	3	4	5
11	Emotional immaturity	0	1	2	3	4	5
12	Withdrawn, timid, or appears fearful toward change and transition	0	1	2	3	4	5

13	Exhibits ADD or ADHD tendencies	0	1	2	3	4	5
14	Difficulty with social skills (e.g. may appear fearful to join in or doesn't know how to join a game with friends; extra difficulty with age-appropriate interactions, becomes anxious and worried when anticipating others' reactions)	0	1	2	3	4	5
15	Depression and/or feeling down	0	1	2	3	4	5
16	Difficulty making decisions	0	1	2	3	4	5
17	Poor balance and coordination (e.g. difficulty with sports, ball games, climbing structures)	0	1	2	3	4	5
18	Needs to control games or outcomes (e.g. rigidity, manipulates situations to have a certain outcome, might be insecure)	0	1	2	3	4	5
19	Muscle tension (e.g. body feels "on guard")	0	1	2	3	4	5
20	Other health issues (e.g. allergies, asthma, and adrenal fatigue, poor digestion, or food sensitivities)	0	1	2	3	4	5

Note: Usually one retained reflex leads to retention in other reflexes. To be safe, work on all of the primitive reflexes. Before working with a child, go through the symptoms checklist, and rate the severity of the symptoms or behaviors on a scale of 0-5, 0 being "not seen" to 5 being "severe."

For downloadable version, visit
symptoms-checklist-moro.polaristherapy.com.

THE STARFISH EXERCISE SCREEN

You can use the following Starfish exercise as part of the screening process to determine if further testing is needed.

1. Parent or therapist should first demonstrate the starfish exercise (refer to exercises #1 and #2).

2. Have the child sit on a chair or beanbag, and ask them to curl up. They might cross opposite arms and legs for the first try. Observe and note these patterns.

3. Show them how to curl up by crossing the right leg over the left leg and right arm over the left arm.

4. Ask them to do the exercise as demonstrated on the opposite side.

Inability to perform this exercise well may be a sign of a retained Moro reflex.

CHAPTER 4

A. INTERVENTION AND TREATMENT PLANNING

Choose an intervention method that works best for each child. One of the best ways to help integrate primitive reflexes is by mimicking early childhood movement patterns. The exercises compiled in this book are for those who are receiving occupational therapy or other reflex integration treatments. Use them as a daily home program and as movement breaks in a school setting with the help of a trained professional.

Note: With a retained Moro reflex, the child will continue to be stimuli-responsive or hypersensitive to sounds, sudden movement, etc. While working to integrate the Moro, advise and educate teachers and care providers to be sensitive to the child's sensory needs. The following are some strategies and accommodations to support the child during Moro integration therapy.

B. ACCOMMODATIONS

A child with retained Moro reflex is over-reactive to stimuli and reacts emotionally. Choose one or more of the following accommodations to meet the child's needs.

1. Create a safe home/office environment or non-threatening classroom.

2. Create structure and consistency for the day. A clear structure makes a child's day predictable and reduces stress.

3. Use a visual schedule the child can refer to throughout the day.

4. Reduce noises to a minimum. Use sound-reducing headphones during focused work time, but do not make a habit of having the child wear them all the time.

5. Reduce the level of sudden movements (visual stimuli) to a minimum. Place the child in a corner where nothing can "sneak out" behind him.

6. Position the child away from busy classroom areas. Face the door instead of their back to the door.

7. Use positive reinforcement. Retained Moro heightens the emotional state and makes self-esteem a big issue, so do not focus on the child's shortcomings, but instead work on building confidence by reinforcing his or her strengths.

8. Do not force activities that might trigger anxiety in the child. Instead, break down tasks, and slowly build on them.

9. Provide frequent movement breaks that target the Moro reflex. Make the child's daily tasks accessible and flexible to accommodate movement breaks.

10. Position the child away from alarms and speakerphones.

C. EXERCISES TO PROMOTE MORO REFLEX INTEGRATION

The exercises below can be used in the order you think is best for your student/child. Follow the order presented here, or combine the exercises with others during your session. The manner in which you utilize the exercises depends on the environment, the child's state, and materials you have on hand. For example, make the activities fun and exciting when working with younger children, but feel free to create more of a workout session with older students and adults. Avoid frustration and anxiety. As much as possible, try to make the exercises fun and enjoyable. For kids who are younger and refuse to cooperate, incorporate the use of positive reinforcement or rewards to encourage participation.

Note: the exercises challenge more than one of the primitive reflexes, including the Moro reflex, encourage bilateral coordination, spatial awareness, and motor planning skills. Do these games and activities during the child's therapy sessions, daily movement breaks, and home exercise program.

I have added additional modifications and accommodations for exercises that many students find difficult. You can incorporate those steps, but they are not always necessary.

1) THE STARFISH ON BEANBAG

MATERIALS: Large beanbag, cushions, or large pillow

1. Start with the child sitting on the edge of the beanbag/cushion/pillow.

2. Have the child spread arms and legs while simultaneously leaning and looking back.

3. Hold for 5 seconds.

4. Have the child bring chin to chest, and lift up by bringing the body into a curled position, with the right arm crossing over the left arm and right leg crossed over the left leg, head down with eyes gazing downward.

5. Hold for 5 seconds.

6. Repeat by spreading arms and legs like a starfish and leaning back.

7. Hold for 5 seconds.

8. Bring the body into a curled position, first with left arm crossing over right arm and left leg crossing over right leg, then again with head down, eyes gazing downward.

9. Hold for 5 seconds.

10. Repeat the entire sequence 10 times.

GOALS:

1. Complete smooth and controlled movement independently

2. Body awareness (right and left side discrimination)

3. Bilateral coordination

4. Motor planning and sequencing

POSITIVE SIGNS:

- ☐ Fluid and controlled movement

- ☐ Right and left side discrimination

- ☐ Able to sequence movements

- ☐ Able to tilt the head back without uneasiness

- ☐ Able to bring head up independently

NEGATIVE SIGNS:

- ☐ Uneven movement; one side moves faster than the other

- ☐ Unable to tilt head back

- ☐ Unable to bring head up and curl body inward

- ☐ Unable to sequence movements correctly

- ☐ Dizziness or nauseousness

2) STARFISH ON CHAIR

MATERIALS: Chair

1. Start with the child sitting on a chair.

2. Have the child spread out arms and legs while simultaneously leaning back with eyes looking back.

3. Hold for 5 seconds.

4. Have the child bring the body in flexion position with right arm crossing over left, right leg crosses over left leg, and head flexed in a curled position.

5. Hold for 5 seconds.

6. Repeat by spreading arms and legs like a starfish and lean back.

7. Hold for 5 seconds.

8. Bring body back in flexion with head looking downward; this time left arm crosses over the right arm, and left leg crosses over the right leg

9. Hold for 5 seconds.

10. Repeat the entire sequence 5-7 times.

GOALS:

1. Complete a smooth and controlled starfish movement independently

2. Bilateral coordination and body awareness

3. Motor planning and sequencing

POSITIVE SIGNS:

- ☐ Fluid and controlled movement

- ☐ Right and left side discrimination

- ☐ Able to sequence movements

- ☐ Able to tilt head back without discomfort

- ☐ Able to bring head up independently

NEGATIVE SIGNS:

- ☐ Uneven movement; one side moves faster than the other

- ☐ Unable to tilt head back

- ☐ Unable to bring head up and curl body in

- ☐ Unable to sequence movements correctly

- ☐ Dizziness or nauseousness

3) STARFISH STANDING

MATERIALS: None

1. Start with the child standing.

2. Have the child spread out arms and legs while simultaneously leaning head back with eyes looking up.

3. Hold for 5 seconds.

4. Have the child bring their body into a half-squat position with right arm crossing over left, right leg crossing over left leg, and head flexed in a curled position.

5. Hold for 5 seconds.

6. Repeat by standing and spreading arms and legs like a starfish, lifting head and looking up.

7. Hold for 5 seconds.

8. Bring the body back to a half-squat, with head looking down; this time left arm crosses over the right arm, and left leg crosses over the right leg.

9. Hold for 5 seconds.

10. Repeat the entire sequence 5-7 times.

GOALS:

1. Complete a smooth and controlled starfish movement independently

2. Balance and bilateral coordination

3. Motor planning and sequencing

4. Body awareness and right and left side coordination

POSITIVE SIGNS:

- ☐ Balance

- ☐ Fluid and controlled movement

- ☐ Right and left side discrimination

- ☐ Able to sequence movements

- ☐ Able to tilt head back without discomfort

- ☐ Able to bring head up independently

NEGATIVE SIGNS:

- ☐ Uneven movement; one side moves faster than the other

- ☐ Unable to tilt head back

- ☐ Unable to bring head up and curl body inward

- ☐ Unable to sequence movements correctly

- ☐ Dizziness or nauseousness

4) BRIDGE

MATERIALS: Yoga mat and small ball

1. Have the child lay supine on the floor with knees bent and feet flat on the ground.

2. Direct the child to place palms together in prayer position resting on the chest. (Use a small ball between palms if necessary.)

3. Push hands together while keeping the shoulders on the floor, and simultaneously lift the hips off the ground to the bridge position.

4. Hold this position for 5-7 seconds.

5. Slowly bring hips down to the mat, keeping the hands still on the chest.

6. Rest for 5-7 seconds.

7. Repeat the entire sequence 7-10 times.

TIP: Give a child a small light ball to press between palms while holding the bridge.

GOALS:

1. Complete a smooth and controlled bridge exercise independently

2. Bilateral coordination

3. Motor planning

POSITIVE SIGNS:

☐ Fluid and controlled movements

☐ Able to hold a bridge pose

☐ Able to stabilize hands on chest and maintain equal pressure

NEGATIVE SIGNS:

- ☐ Hands sliding or lifting off the chest

- ☐ Body rocking or falling

- ☐ Unable to lift body up to bridge pose

- ☐ Tension in shoulder and neck area

5) SPLAT

MATERIALS: Yoga mat

1. Have the child lay supine on the floor with knees bent, feet flat on the ground, and arms raised straight up to the ceiling.

2. While both arms are still raised, lift hips up to hold a bridge.

3. Hold for 3 seconds.

4. With one smooth movement, have the child "splat" to the floor by lowering the arms and hips to meet the floor while straightening the legs.

5. Hold for 3 seconds.

6. Repeat the entire sequence 5-7 times.

GOALS:

1. Complete a smooth and controlled splat movement independently.

2. Develop bilateral coordination and body awareness.

POSITIVE SIGNS:

☐ Fluid and controlled movements

☐ Able to hold a bridge pose with arms straight up to the ceiling

☐ Able to sequence both arms and legs equally

☐ Stable and balanced body

NEGATIVE SIGNS:

- ☐ Arms not held up equally

- ☐ Body rocking or falling

- ☐ Unable to lift the body up to bridge pose

- ☐ Unable to sequence arms and legs at the same speed

- ☐ Tension in the shoulder and neck area

6) DUCK WALK HOLDING A STICK

MATERIALS: Shoulder-length stick and pictures of feet cutouts for visual cues

1. Stand with heels touching and toes pointed outward in a "V" position.

2. Hold the stick with palms down, both thumbs pointing towards each other.

3. Walk forward like a duck (keeping feet in a "V" position) for about 15 feet, keeping the stick level.

4. Pause for 3 seconds.

5. Walk backward like a duck (keeping feet in a "V" position) for about 15 feet keeping the stick level.

6. Repeat 3-5 times.

GOALS:

1. Walk forward and backward with a smooth and natural motion.

2. Maintain a steady and balanced stick throughout the exercise.

3. Demonstrate right and left side discrimination.

When this level is reached at an acceptable skill level, transition to the next pigeon/duck exercise.

POSITIVE SIGNS:

☐ Able to keep stick level

☐ Upright posture

☐ Smooth and fluid movements

☐ Right and left foot turned out at equal angles

☐ Able to walk forward and backward

NEGATIVE SIGNS:

☐ Arms and hands turning out

☐ Stick not level to the floor

☐ Feet straightening out

☐ Unable to sequence movements

☐ Grimacing or tongue sticking out

☐ Tension in neck and shoulder

☐ Losing balance or falling

TIPS FOR DUCK AND PIGEON:

- For extra assistance, print out feet silhouettes, and place them on the floor. Once the child improves, ask them to walk like a duck without any visual cues.

- If activities are challenging for the child, try the modifications below.

HOW TO MODIFY DUCK AND PIGEON
SEATED DUCK AND PIGEON

1. While sitting on a chair with proper posture, have the child bring one foot outward like a duck and inward like a pigeon.

2. Hold for 3 seconds in each position.

3. Repeat 10 times.

4. Repeat step one but with the alternate foot only.

When the child can smoothly execute these exercises, advance to the following:

5. While remaining seated on the chair with proper posture, have the child bring both feet outward like a duck and inward like a pigeon.

6. Hold for 3 seconds in each position.

7. Repeat 10 times.

DUCK AND PIGEON HAND PLACEMENT

1. Sitting with feet comfortably on the floor and in proper posture, have the child hold a stick with palms down and thumbs facing each other.

2. Switch the right hand by holding the stick from the bottom with the palm facing up and thumb pointing out.

3. Do the same with the left hand.

4. Bring the right hand back to the original position.

5. Bring the left hand back to the original position.

6. Repeat 10 times.

*If additional modification is needed, you can work on one side of the body, and increase the number of repetitions until the child completes at least five on both sides.

7) PIGEON WALK HOLDING A STICK

MATERIALS: Shoulder-length stick and pictures of feet cutouts for visual cues

1. Stand in the pigeon position with feet turned inward and heels apart.

2. Hold the stick with thumbs facing outward.

3. Walk forward like a pigeon for about 15 feet, maintaining the position of the stick.

4. Pause for 3 seconds.

5. Walk backward like a pigeon for about 15 feet, maintaining the position of the stick.

6. Repeat 3-5 times.

GOALS:

1. Able to walk forward and backward with a smooth and natural motion

2. Maintain a steady and balanced stick throughout the exercise

3. Right and left side discrimination

POSITIVE SIGNS:

- ☐ Able to keep stick level

- ☐ Upright posture

- ☐ Smooth and fluid movements

- ☐ Both feet turned equally

- ☐ Able to walk forward and backward

NEGATIVE SIGNS:

- ☐ Arms and hands turning inward

- ☐ Stick not level to the floor

- ☐ Feet straightening out

- ☐ Unable to sequence movements

- ☐ Grimacing or tongue sticking out

- ☐ Tension to neck and shoulder

- ☐ Losing balance or falling

8) DUCK WALK HOLDING A MARKER

MATERIALS: Same color markers and pictures of feet cutouts for visual cues

1. Stand with heels touching and toes turned outward in a "V" position.

2. Hold the marker with palms down and tops facing each other, both thumbs toward the marker top.

3. Walk forward like a duck for about 15 feet maintaining the position of the marker.

4. Walk backward like a duck for about 15 feet maintaining the position of the marker.

5. Repeat 3-5 times.

GOALS:

1. Able to walk forward and backward with smooth and controlled movement

2. Maintain a steady and balanced marker throughout the exercise

3. Right and left side discrimination

POSITIVE SIGNS:

- [ ] Able to keep markers level

- [ ] Upright posture

- [ ] Smooth and fluid movements

- [ ] Right and left foot turned out equally

- [ ] Able to walk forward and backward

NEGATIVE SIGNS:

- [ ] Arms and hands turning outward

- [ ] Unable to keep thumbs and markers facing each other and parallel to the floor

- [ ] Feet straightening out

- [ ] Unable to sequence movements

- [ ] Grimacing or tongue sticking out

- [ ] Tension to neck and shoulder

- [ ] Losing balance or falling

9) PIGEON WALK HOLDING A MARKER

MATERIALS: Same color markers and pictures of feet cutouts for visual cues

1. Stand in the pigeon position with feet turned inward and heels apart.

2. Hold the marker with thumbs and marker top facing outward.

3. Walk forward like a pigeon for about 15 feet, maintaining the position of the marker.

4. Walk backward like a pigeon for about 15 feet, maintaining the position of the marker.

5. Repeat 3-5 times.

GOALS:

1. Able to walk forward and backward with a smooth and controlled movement

2. Maintain a steady and balanced marker throughout the exercise

3. Right and left side discrimination

When the child can perform these movements comfortably, transition to the next pigeon/duck exercise.

POSITIVE SIGNS:

☐ Able to keep markers level

☐ Upright posture

☐ Smooth and fluid movements

☐ Hold right and left foot in similar positions

☐ Able to walk forward and backward

NEGATIVE SIGNS:

☐ Arms and hands turning inward

☐ Unable to keep markers level to the floor and facing away from each other

☐ Feet straightening out

☐ Unable to sequence movements

☐ Grimacing or tongue sticking out

☐ Tension in neck and shoulder

☐ Losing balance or falling

10) DUCK WALK WITHOUT HOLDING ANYTHING

MATERIALS: Pictures of feet cutouts for visual cues

1. Stand with heels touching and toes outward in "V" position.

2. Close both fists, palms facing down, thumbs straight and facing each other.

3. Walk forward like a duck for about 15 feet, maintaining the position of both thumbs.

4. Walk backward like a duck for about 15 feet, maintaining the position of both thumbs.

5. Repeat 3-5 times.

GOALS:

1. Able to walk forward and backward with a smooth and natural motion.

2. Maintain steady and balanced hands throughout the exercise.

3. Right and left side discrimination.

POSITIVE SIGNS:

- ☐ Able to keep thumbs parallel to the floor and facing toward each other

- ☐ Upright posture

- ☐ Smooth and fluid movements

- ☐ Able to maintain feet in a "V" shape while walking

- ☐ Able to walk forward and backward

NEGATIVE SIGNS:

- ☐ Arms and hands turning out

- ☐ Thumbs not parallel to the floor and facing each other

- ☐ Feet straightening out

- ☐ Unable to sequence movements

- ☐ Grimacing or tongue sticking out

- ☐ Tension to neck and shoulder

- ☐ Losing balance or falling

11) PIGEON WALK WITHOUT HOLDING ANYTHING

MATERIALS: Pictures of feet cutouts for visual cues

1. Stand in the pigeon position with feet turned inward and heels apart.

2. Close both fists, palms facing down, thumbs straight and facing outward.

3. Walk forward like a pigeon for about 15 feet, maintaining the position of the thumbs.

4. Walk backward like a pigeon for about 15 feet, maintaining the position of the thumbs.

5. Repeat 3-5 times.

GOALS:

1. Able to walk forward and backward with a smooth and natural motion

2. Maintain steady and balanced hands throughout the exercise

3. Right and left side discrimination

POSITIVE SIGNS:

- ☐ Able to keep thumbs parallel to the floor and facing away from each other

- ☐ Upright posture

- ☐ Smooth and fluid movements

- ☐ Able to maintain feet in a turned inward position

- ☐ Able to walk forward and backward

NEGATIVE SIGNS:

- ☐ Arms and hands turning inward

- ☐ Thumbs not level to the floor and each other

- ☐ Feet straightening out

- ☐ Unable to sequence movements

- ☐ Grimacing or tongue sticking out

- ☐ Tension in neck and shoulder

- ☐ Losing balance or falling

12) DUCK AND PIGEON HOP HOLDING A MARKER

MATERIALS: Two same color markers

1. Stand in the duck position with heels touching and toes facing out and hands down with thumbs and marker caps facing each other.

2. Jump and switch to pigeon position with toes touching and heels separate and palms facing up while thumbs and marker caps are facing away from each other.

3. Jump back to duck position (Step 1).

4. Repeat 5-7 times.

GOALS:

1. Complete 7-10 consecutive Duck and Pigeon Hop exercises

2. Maintain steady and balanced hands throughout the exercises

3. Right and left side discrimination

4. Motor planning and bilateral coordination

When this level is reached at an acceptable ability, the child is done working on pigeon/duck exercises.

POSITIVE SIGNS:

- ☐ Able to motor plan sequence

- ☐ Upright posture

- ☐ Smooth and fluid movements

- ☐ Equal right and left side movements

- ☐ Hands moving at the same time and speed

- ☐ Feet moving at the same time and speed

NEGATIVE SIGNS:

- ☐ Unequal arm movement

- ☐ Unequal feet movement

- ☐ Unable to jump

- ☐ Markers not leveled to the floor

☐ Feet straightening out

☐ Unable to sequence movements

☐ Grimacing or tongue sticking out

☐ Tension to neck and shoulder

☐ Losing balance or falling

13) DUCK AND PIGEON HOP WITHOUT A MARKER

MATERIALS: None

1. Stand in duck position with heels touching and toes facing out and hands down with thumbs facing each other.

2. Jump and switch to pigeon position with toes touching and heels separate and palms facing up while thumbs are facing away from each other.

3. Jump back to duck position (Step 1).

4. Repeat 5-7 times.

GOALS:

1. Jump at least 5-7 times in a row

2. Maintain steady and balanced hands throughout the exercise

3. Right and left side discrimination

4. Motor planning and bilateral coordination

POSITIVE SIGNS:

- ☐ Able to motor plan sequence

- ☐ Upright posture

- ☐ Smooth and fluid movements

- ☐ Equal right and left side movements

- ☐ Hands moving at the same time and speed

- ☐ Feet moving at the same time and speed

NEGATIVE SIGNS:

- ☐ Unequal arms movement

- ☐ Unequal feet movement

- ☐ Unable to jump

- ☐ Thumbs not level to the floor

- ☐ Feet straightening out

- ☐ Unable to sequence movements

- ☐ Grimacing or tongue sticking out

- ☐ Tension in neck and shoulder

- ☐ Losing balance or falling

14) EARTH HUGGER (FORWARD)

MATERIALS: Yoga mat

1. Have the child lay face down on the mat with arms extended.

2. Ask the child to press down as if giving a full-body hug to the floor.

3. Check to see if the child is pressing down by lightly lifting arms and legs upward.

4. Have the child hold that position while you are checking for 10 seconds.

5. Repeat 5-7 times.

6. Advanced: ask the child to lift only the head while pressing down the floor with arms and legs

*Head must face down. The turning of the head to the right or the left will activate the Asymmetrical Tonic Neck Reflex (ATNR). If necessary, provide physical head support to maintain face down position. This exercise can help integrate the Tonic Labyrinthine Reflex (TLR).

GOALS:

1. Maintain equal resistance in all four extremities

2. Coordination of both sides of the body

3. Body awareness

POSITIVE SIGNS:

☐   Able to motor plan sequence

☐   Equal pressure in all extremities

☐   Able to lift head

NEGATIVE SIGNS:

☐   Unable to press down equally with both arms and legs

☐   Unequal pressure within the extremities

☐   Unable to lift head

15) EARTH HUGGER (BACKWARDS)

MATERIALS: Yoga mat

1. Have the child lay face up on the mat with arms extended.

2. Ask the child to press down as if pushing the floor downward.

3. Check to see if the child is pressing down by lightly trying to lift arms and legs upward.

4. Have the child hold that position while you check arms and legs for 10 seconds.

5. Repeat 5-7 times.

6. Advanced: ask the child to lift only the head while pressing down the floor with arms and legs

*The child's head must face up. The turning of the head to the right or the left will activate the Asymmetrical Tonic Neck Reflex (ATNR). If necessary, provide physical head support to maintain face up position. This exercise can help integrate the Tonic Labyrinthine Reflex (TLR).

GOALS:

1. Maintain equal resistance in all four extremities

2. Coordination of both sides of the body

3. Body awareness

POSITIVE SIGNS:

- ☐ Able to motor plan sequence

- ☐ Equal pressure in all extremities

- ☐ Able to lift head

NEGATIVE SIGNS:

- ☐ Unable to press down equally with both arms and legs

- ☐ Unable to differentiate the right side of the body from the left side of the body

- ☐ Unable to lift head

16) POPCORN ON FLOOR

MATERIALS: Yoga mat

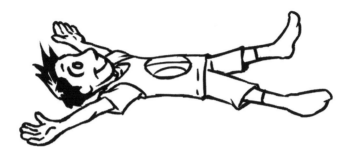

1. Have the child lie down, supine on a yoga mat, with arms and legs extended

2. Encourage the child to bring chin to the chest, and curl up by supporting knees with hands.

3. Hold for 3-5 seconds.

4. In a smooth and controlled movement, have the child bring the body back to its original position.

5. Repeat 5-10 times.

GOALS:

1. Complete 7-10 consecutive Popcorn on Floor exercises independently

2. Bilateral coordination

3. Upper-body strengthening

POSITIVE SIGNS:

☐ Ability to lift the head off the floor and maintain head flexion independently

☐ Ability to balance body without rocking side-to-side when curled up

☐ Fluid arm and leg movements

NEGATIVE SIGNS:

- ☐ Head lagging behind when trying to curl up

- ☐ Body rocking left to right

- ☐ Unable to bring body into a curled position

- ☐ Facial grimacing or tongue sticking out

- ☐ Tension in neck and shoulders

17) POPCORN ON THERAPY BALL

MATERIALS: Yoga mat and therapy ball

1. Have the child sit balanced on a therapy ball. (Give physical support if child cannot balance independently.)

2. Have the child lean backward, dropping the head as far back as possible while stretching arms out.

3. Hold for three seconds.

4. With smooth and controlled movement, bring upper body upright, pull arms inward in a curled position, and drop head toward the navel.

5. Hold for 3-5 seconds.

6. Repeat 5-7 times.

GOALS:

1. Complete 5-7 consecutive Popcorn on Therapy Ball exercises in a smooth and controlled manner.

2. Complete the task without feeling dizzy, fearful, or nauseous.

POSITIVE SIGNS:

- ☐ Ability to drop head back with arms spread out

- ☐ Ability to lift head and curl forward

- ☐ Ability to balance body

- ☐ Fluidity of movement

NEGATIVE SIGNS:

- ☐ Signs of dizziness or nausea

- ☐ Hesitation and fear when the head tilts back

- ☐ Tension in neck and shoulders

18) HUG A BALL

MATERIALS: Yoga mat and a large ball

1. Have the child lie down on their backside on the mat.

2. Have the child hold a large ball in place with arms and legs and with head on the floor (bend knees if necessary).

3. Give slight resistance to the ball as if you are trying to take it away, so the child maintains a hold on the ball.

4. Hold for 5-7 seconds.

5. Repeat 7-10 times.

GOALS:

1. Coordination of both sides of the body

2. Body awareness

3. Maintaining constant pressure to hold the ball in place to build strength

POSITIVE SIGNS:

☐ Able to coordinate both sides of the body

☐ Equal pressure in all extremities

☐ Able to balance ball between arms and legs

NEGATIVE SIGNS:

☐ Unable to maintain equal pressure in all extremities

☐ Unable to balance the ball without attempting to grab it with hands

19) HUG A BALL: ALTERNATING ARMS AND LEGS

MATERIALS: Yoga mat and a large ball

1. Have the child lie down on their backside on the mat.

2. Have the child hold a large ball in place with one arm and one leg and with head on the floor. (Bend knees if necessary.)

   a. Same side: right arm and right leg

b. Same side: left arm and left leg

c. Opposite sides: right arm and left leg

    d.   Opposite sides: left arm and right leg

3.   Give slight resistance to the ball as if you are trying to take it away, so the child maintains a hold on the ball.

4.   Hold for 5-7 seconds.

5.   Repeat three times for each side.

GOALS:

1.   Coordination of both sides of the body

2.   Body awareness

3.   Upper body and lower body strength

POSITIVE SIGNS:

- ☐ Able to coordinate both sides of the body

- ☐ Able to balance ball between arms and legs

NEGATIVE SIGNS:

- ☐ Unable to coordinate both upper body and lower body movements simultaneously

- ☐ Unable to balance the ball without attempting to grab it with hands

- ☐ Shoulder tension and facial grimaces

20) HOT POTATOES

MATERIALS: Yoga mat and a 12" ball

1. Have the child lie down on the back on the mat.

2. Have the child hold a light basketball-sized ball with both hands over the head.

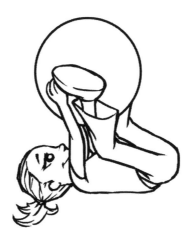

3. Ask the child to transfer the ball from hands to feet.

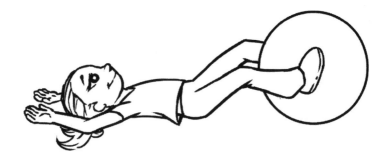

4. Both feet and arms should reach towards the mat without arching the back.

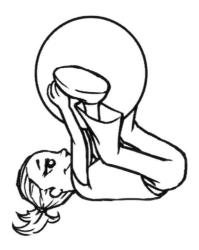

5. Maintaining the hold, pass the ball from feet back to hands.

6. Repeat 5-10 times.

GOALS:

1. Able to bring legs and arms together

2. Isolation and differentiation of legs and arms

3. Improved bilateral coordination

4. Core strength

*This exercise is advanced and requires core strength and is best for older kids and adults.

POSITIVE SIGNS:

☐   Able to coordinate both sides of the body

☐   Able to sustain smooth and controlled movement

☐   Maintain sufficient upper body, trunk, and lower body strength

NEGATIVE SIGNS:

☐   Unable to maintain smooth and controlled movement

☐   Unable to transfer the ball between hands and legs

☐   Shoulder tension and facial grimaces

21) BALL PASS OVER THE HEAD AND BETWEEN LEGS

MATERIALS: various different sized balls

1. Have the student stand with feet shoulder-length apart and with a ball in both hands.

2. Stand behind the student and have them pass the ball overhead, maintaining visual gaze.

3. Pass the ball through the legs, so the child will have to bend down to take it.

4. Do this slowly, so the student doesn't become too dizzy.

5. Repeat 3-5 times and take a break.

GOALS:

1. Maintain a smooth and controlled movement

2. No dizziness, fear of falling, or loss of balance

POSITIVE SIGNS:

☐ Able to coordinate both sides of the body

☐ Able to sustain smooth and controlled movement

☐ Maintaining balance

NEGATIVE SIGNS:

- ☐ Unable to maintain smooth and controlled movement

- ☐ Anxiousness

- ☐ Nauseousness

- ☐ Loss of balance

22) SLITHER LIKE SNAKE ON BACK

MATERIALS: smooth floor to slide around

1. Have the child lie down on the floor on their back with both arms flat on the floor. (Note: Observe the way the student was able to move onto his/her back. Was there any discomfort? Was there any hesitation, confusion, or anxiety?)

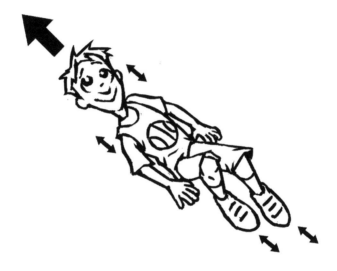

2. While keeping both feet on the ground, have the child push down into the ground with their feet and hands to propel themselves backward. If necessary, place a visual target overhead for the child to follow.

3. Have the student "slither" in this manner for approximately 15-20 feet.

4. *You can use this activity as an obstacle course game. For example, slither under a table.

GOALS:

1. Complete 15-20 feet of slithering

2. Bilateral coordination and motor planning

3. Visual perception and body awareness

POSITIVE SIGNS:

☐ Able to coordinate both sides of the body

☐ Able to gaze overhead

☐ Able to sustain smooth and controlled movement

☐ Able to follow a marked path (visual perception and spatial orientation)

NEGATIVE SIGNS:

☐ Unable to maintain smooth and controlled movement

☐ Anxiousness

☐ Appearing disoriented

☐ Lifts head to check direction instead of moving instinctively

There are several ways to play this game. If you're using a long table, you can place stickers or tape small treasures under the table for the child to find. Ask the child to slither backward and collect the treasures. Make sure the child is looking overhead and using feet to move backward.

The goal of this exercise is to help the child feel comfortable in this position and to push the ground with both feet and hands while on their back. Play this game as part of the Earth Hugger Backward.

23) BALLOON TOSS

MATERIALS: Balloon

1. Give the child a balloon, and play toss the balloon overhead for a few minutes.

2. If the child does not have sufficient balance, start in a seated position, and play volleyball.

3. When the child has better balance or is in a cushioned environment, play volleyball with the balloon.

Balloons are an excellent prop since they travel more slowly than a rubber ball, and give the child time to react. Encourage the child to look up overhead to hit and catch the balloon.

VARIATIONS:

a. Catching: Throw a balloon to the child and play catch. Encourage using both hands to catch. This exercise encourages visual tracking (convergence/divergence) and bilateral coordination.

b. <u>Catching and throwing</u>: After catching the balloon, encourage the child to throw it back to you with both hands. This encourages motor planning and aiming.

c. <u>Hitting a moving balloon</u>: Instead of catching with both hands, have your child hit the balloon with their dominant hand. You should then pass the balloon back to them. This will help slow down the speed. You can skip this stage and move to the next if you think your child is ready and will still have fun.

d. <u>Hitting the balloon back and forth</u>: Don't stop the balloon, and have the child play "volleyball" with you.

e. <u>Throw and catch</u>: Have your child toss the balloon upward and catch it, repeating this several times. This exercise encourages vertical tracking, eye-hand coordination, and motor planning.

f. "Juggle" the balloon: Have the child hit the balloon up in the air repeatedly without catching it. This activity can be difficult since it challenges the vestibular system, and kids with balance challenges might have difficulty maintaining their balance. It encourages vertical tracking, speed, motor planning, and body awareness.

g. Alternate hands while hitting a moving balloon: Specify the hand with which you'd like the child to catch the ball. This encourages eye-hand coordination, motor planning, and body awareness.

h. Have fun!

GOALS:

1. Visual skills: visual tracking, focusing, and peripheral vision

2. Maintaining balance

3. Hand-eye coordination

4. Spatial orientation

5. Motor planning

POSITIVE SIGNS:

- ☐ Able to coordinate both sides of the body to catch and hit the balloon

- ☐ Able to sustain smooth and controlled visual tracking skills

NEGATIVE SIGNS:

- ☐ Unable to maintain smooth and controlled movement

- ☐ Unable to visually track the balloon

- ☐ Appearing disoriented

- ☐ Dizziness

- ☐ Facial grimaces and movement overflows

24) GROWING TREE

MATERIALS: None

1. Start by having the child stand with back straight.

2. Have the child squat down with head tucked in and eyes looking down (pretending to be a "seed").

3. Hold for 3-5 seconds.

4. Have the child slowly bring the body to standing, open legs and arms in the shape of the letter X, and look up ("growing tree").

5. Hold for 3-5 seconds.

6. Repeat 5-7 times.

GOALS:

1. Maintain a smooth transition from "seed" to "tree"

2. Complete 5-7 consecutive Growing Tree exercises

POSITIVE SIGNS:

☐ Ability to stay balanced

☐ Ability to bring both arms and legs together

☐ Ability to tilt back the head independently

☐ Ability to differentiate right and left parts of the body

NEGATIVE SIGNS:

☐ Dizziness or nausea

☐ Loss of balance

☐ Inability to coordinate movement

☐ Disorientation and confusion

25) MONKEY BARS

MATERIALS: Monkey bars or trapeze

1. Ask the child to hang from monkey bars or trapeze for 5-10 seconds.

2. Rest.

3. If possible, ask the student to complete a few rounds of hanging on the monkey bars. You can modify this by giving the child physical support.

GOALS:

1. Ability to grasp the bar and hang while looking up

2. Alternating hands opening and closing skills, which encourages Palmar reflex and integration and inhibition of the Moro reflex

POSITIVE SIGNS:

☐ Ability to hold on to monkey bar for 5-10 seconds

☐ Ability to look at monkey bar while holding on to the bars

☐ Ability to alternate hands opening and closing while hanging on to the bars

NEGATIVE SIGNS:

- ☐ Anxious or nervous giggle

- ☐ Unable to close hands and hold on

- ☐ Excessive fear, even with extra physical support

- ☐ Hands seem to jerk away from the bars

Note: A child with retained Moro reflex might not be able to hang from monkey bars or trapeze for more than a few seconds or not at all due to gravitational insecurities and retained Moro (i.e. hands opening instead of grasping and underdeveloped Palmar reflex. The Palmar reflex helps with gripping and helps inhibits the Moro reflex.)

MODIFICATION

- ☐ Encourage the child to hold on to the bar using the hand-over-hand method for 3-5 seconds.

- ☐ Gradually increase or decrease the level of physical support.

26) BANANA KICKS

MATERIALS: Soccer ball

1. Instruct the child to kick a soccer ball using the inside of the foot.

2. Kick 7-10 times using right foot.

3. Kick 7-10 times using left foot.

GOALS:

1. Ability to externally rotate one leg while the remaining body stay neutral

2. Motor plan to hit a ball using the inside of the foot

POSITIVE SIGNS:

☐ Fluid movement and coordination

☐ Able to move one leg at a time

NEGATIVE SIGNS:

☐ Unable to externally rotate feet

☐ Movement overflow (e.g. awkward body twisting, facial grimace, etc.)

☐ Unable to differentiate right from left

27) ROCKING ON THERAPY BALL

MATERIALS: Big therapy ball

1. Have the student cross arms and sit on the therapy ball.

2. Have the student lean back, place their entire weight on a big therapy ball, and extend arms.

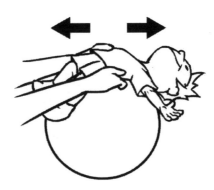

3. Gently push the ball, so the child's feet leave the floor. Make sure you can balance and hold on to the student.

4. Rock back and forth and side to side for approximately 7-10 seconds.

5. Rest.

GOALS:

1. Able to keep arms crossed the entire time

2. Balance

3. Postural control

POSITIVE SIGNS

☐ Ability to rock back and forth and maintain balance

☐ Able to lean back and extend arms without stress

☐ Enjoying activity

NEGATIVE SIGNS

☐ Unable to keep arms crossed

☐ Unable to keep balance

☐ Anxiety and panic

If you work in an occupational therapy clinic, you will have access to a variety of equipment. Pieces of equipment that challenge your student to hold on with both arms and legs while swinging are great therapeutic exercises to integrate and challenge retained reflexes, including the Moro reflex.

28) HORIZONTAL BOLSTER SWINGS

MATERIALS: bolster swing

1.   Start by having the child hold on to the swing while laying flat on their tummy.

2.   Gently move the swing.

3. Encourage the child to continue holding, but begin to turn upside down.

4. Encourage the child to hold onto the swing while it is moving.

(If the child has good balance and is not anxious to move on to the next phase, continue to challenge him or her.)

5. Have the child hold the swing upside down for about 5-7 seconds. Make sure to catch the child if necessary.

29) DIAGONAL BOLSTER SWINGS

1. Secure the bolster at approximately 45 degrees.

2. Repeat steps one and two.

3. Encourage the child to flip over, and continue to hang on to the swing while upside down.

4. For a more advanced challenge, have the child climb upside down while on a swing that is secured at 45 degrees.

GOALS:

1. Strengthening, postural control, and balance

2. Bilateral coordination

POSITIVE SIGNS

- ☐ Able to hold on to swing and maintain balance

- ☐ Show adequate postural control

- ☐ Enjoying activity

NEGATIVE SIGNS

- ☐ Unable to maintain balance

- ☐ Falls off

- ☐ Anxiety and panic

30) MOON SWING

MATERIALS: Moon swing

1. Use the swing as is. Encourage the child to climb on, and wrap legs and arms around the swing to hold on.

2. Gently move the swing.

3. Encourage the child to continue holding and balancing, as you increase the speed at which you push the swing.

GOALS:

1. Increasing strength, postural control, and balance

2. Bilateral coordination

POSITIVE SIGNS

- ☐ Able to hold on to swing and maintain balance

- ☐ Show adequate postural control

- ☐ Strong grips

NEGATIVE SIGNS

- ☐ Unable to maintain balance

- ☐ Falls off

- ☐ Anxiety and panic

31) MOON SWING AND TRAPEZE

MATERIALS: Moon swing and trapeze

1. Create an obstacle course with a trapeze to have the child transfer from a trapeze to the moon swing without touching the floor.

2. Have the child swing from a trapeze, and grab the moon swing with legs.

3. Once the legs are securely grabbing the moon swing, encourage the child to transfer hands from trapeze to the moon swing.

GOALS:

1. Increasing strength, postural control, and balance

2. Bilateral coordination

3. Motor planning

POSITIVE SIGNS

- ☐ Able to hold on to swing and maintain balance

- ☐ Show adequate postural control

- ☐ Able to transfer from Trapeze to Moon swing

- ☐ Enjoying activity

NEGATIVE SIGNS

- ☐ Unable to swing from trapeze to moon swing

- ☐ Unable to maintain balance

- ☐ Falls off

- ☐ Anxiety and panic

CHAPTER 5

ADDITIONAL RECOMMENDATIONS AND RESOURCES

A. HOW DO YOU KNOW IF EXERCISES ARE WORKING?

Parents usually have a harder time seeing the gradual changes their children are making with treatment. While working with my own son, I observe significantly more changes in him than my husband does. This is because I can maintain professional distance, whereas my husband is too close to our son to observe his progress. Because parents often view their children subjectively, I created a checklist to help parents more objectively see their child's development. The same list can also be used to determine if treatment is not working. At times, a child may regress, and this should prompt the care provider to change the approach to treatment.

To make this routine easier for non-professionals to implement, I have created an additional list for monitoring progress and a letter of encouragement to parents who are working on the Moro reflex with their child. The following list is one that I created with my own children and the students with whom I've worked. Make sure to add other symptoms and areas that you might observe. This list can also include goals you are working on, or goals parents have that relate to the Moro reflex. What is on the list depends on the individual child, and the point is to observe and note visible improvements. After about 4-6 weeks of constant reflex integration exercises, you should begin seeing changes. If for any reason there is no improvement, go back and examine your treatment plan.

B. SUGGESTED MOVEMENT BREAKS TO HELP WITH MORO INTEGRATION

To increase the frequency of and exposure to therapeutic exercises, it will be beneficial to have additional movement breaks that target the Moro reflex throughout the child's day. One way to do this is by creating the child's sensory breaks to address the Moro reflex.

While creating the child's sensory and movement activities, be careful not to overwhelm the nervous system. You want the child to ease into movements, and preferably initiate the actions. Give the child options. These sensory breaks should be focused on integrating the Moro reflex gently, not challenging the child to the point of frustration. Please use your clinical judgment and knowledge of the child while you are creating this plan. Below are suggested activities to get you started.

TABLE #2: SUGGESTED MOVEMENT BREAKS TO INCORPORATE THROUGHOUT THE DAY

VESTIBULAR	TACTILE & AUDITORY

• Rolling left and right on a straight line
• Summersault
• Starfish exercises
• Growing tree exercise
• Rocking on therapy ball
• Ball pass overhead and under legs
• Popcorn on floor exercise
• Popcorn on therapy ball exercise
• Riding a scooter board on tummy
• Bolster swing (by trained therapist)
• Moon swing (by trained therapist)
	• Sensory box with different textures
	• If the child has tactile defensiveness, consider the Wilbarger Brushing Protocol
	  ○ Consult with an occupational therapist if this method is being used
	• Music therapy such as the Integrated Listening Systems
	  ○ Consult with an occupational therapist if this method is being used

MOTOR COORDINATION	CALMING TOOLS
• Duck walk • Pigeon walk • Bridge • Splat • Monkey bar • Moon swing and trapeze • All of the exercises in this book can be used for coordination goals	• Quiet Area/Cozy Corner • Calming music • Dim lights • Heavy or weighted blankets that are soft to touch • Walking while wearing a body sock • Stretching in lycra • Activities and obstacle courses that provide deep pressure (prioritize safety!)

For downloadable version, visit
movement-break-moro.polaristherapy.com.

C. TREATMENT IDEAS FOR OCCUPATIONAL THERAPISTS WORKING IN CLINIC SETTING

Table #3: Treatment Ideas for OTs Working in the Clinic

- Bolster swing

- Moon swing

- Hanging down from bolster swing

- Hanging and swinging from a trapeze

- Riding a scooter board on tummy

- Rocking back and forth on a therapy ball

- Sound and music therapy

- Tactile and messy games

- Wilbarger Brushing Protocol

D. LETTER TO PARENT/CAREGIVER

Dear Parents,

When the Moro reflex starts to integrate, you will begin to see improvements and changes in your child's behaviors. However, to make the changes that are needed, you should practice the home exercises your occupational therapist assigns for at least 10 minutes per day. If, after four to six weeks of therapy, you do not see any changes in your child, please contact your occupational therapist. You know your child best and will notice the main areas of growth and lack thereof. To help guide you through the process, here are some areas you should observe during the course of treatment.

- Your child may be significantly more at ease during bath time. You may start to see less anxiety about leaning their head back while washing hair.

- If your child is in a swim class, you might see improvement with backstroke, in particular, and less overall hesitation to get in the water and swim.

- Less startled by unexpected noise, touch, or movement

- Willing to try new things

- Your child may start to give you full body hugs that are firmer

- Learning to hang from monkey bars

- Reduced auditory complaints

- Starts to transition between activities more easily

- Less fearful to walk backward

- Better coordination

- More willing to participate in age appropriate activities which otherwise used to be scary

- Begins to tumble and roll better, specifically backward

- Less fearful of doing somersaults and/or backward rolls

- Calms down more quickly from heightened emotional situations or outbursts

TABLE #3: MORO REFLEX INTEGRATION EXERCISE LOG

	Moro Reflex Integration Exercises	Date Introduced	Date Given to Parents	Date Mastered
1	Starfish on beanbag			
2	Starfish on chair			
3	Starfish Standing			
4	Bridge			
5	Splat			
6	Duck walk holding stick			
7	Pigeon walk holding stick			
8	Duck walk holding marker			
9	Pigeon walk holding marker			
10	Duck walk without holding anything			
11	Pigeon walk without holding anything			
12	Duck and Pigeon hop holding markers			
13	Duck and Pigeon Hop without markers			

14	Hug the earth (forward)			
15	Hug the earth (Backward)			
16	Popcorn on floor			
17	Popcorn on therapy ball			
18	Hug a ball			
19	Hug a ball alternating arms and legs			
20	Hot potatoes			
21	Ball pass over the head and between legs			
22	Slither like a snake on backside			
23	Balloon Toss			
24	Growing Tree			
25	Monkey Bars			
26	Banana Kicks			
27	Rocking on Therapy Ball			
28	Horizontal Bolster Swing			
29	Diagonal Bolster Swing			

30	Moon Swing			
31	Moon Swing and Trapeze			

For downloadable version, visit
exercise-log-moro.polaristherapy.com.

GLOSSARY

Asymmetrical Tonic Neck Reflex (ATNR): is a primitive reflex pattern that usually emerges in utero, around 18 weeks, is fully present at birth, and integrates approximately six months after birth. The ATNR is an involuntary reaction to a head turning to one side. ATNR is active when a head turn to one side, causes the arm and leg; the head turned towards to extend (stretch), while the opposite arm and leg, the head turned away from to flex (bend).

Eye-Hand coordination: (also known as hand-eye coordination) is the ability to process visual input to guide the hands to achieve a specific task (e.g. reaching and grasping).

Extension: straightening of body parts.

Flexion: bending of body parts.

Moro Reflex: is a primitive reflex pattern that typically emerges in utero and integrates approximately four months after birth. It is an involuntary reaction to what is perceived as an outside threat. The threatening stimuli can come in via touch, sound, or the feeling of being dropped, which creates a sense of falling. When the child senses these sensations, the reflex causes the fanning and clenching of fingers, spreading or extending the extremities, followed by a quick flexion of extremities, and crying or anger.

Motor Learning: a neurological ability to learn new movement skills through practice and repetition.

Motor Planning: is the ability to understand, plan, and execute a multiple steps movement activities in the correct order.

Primitive Reflexes: are involuntary movement patterns that are present at birth and become dormant or "integrated" before the child reaches 12 months of age. Most reflexes become integrated into a pattern of movement after infancy, so more mature and voluntary movements can emerge.

Proprioceptive sense: an internal sense of body movement and posture wherein we are in space in relation to other objects and the ability to orient self accordingly.

Retained Reflexes: are primitive reflexes that are actively present when they should have been inhibited (dormant).

Right/Left Discrimination: is an internal or external spatial perception, interpretation, and differentiation of sensory information that originated from the left and right side of the body.

Rooting Reflex: is a primitive reflex pattern that typically emerges in utero and integrates approximately three to four months after birth. When the baby's mouth or cheek is stroked, the head turns toward the stroke, and the mouth opens in search of stimuli. If the mouth finds something to grab, the mouth closes over it, and the sucking motion begins.

Palmer (Grasp) Reflex: is a primitive reflex pattern that emerges in utero, at approximately 11 weeks gestation, and integrates approximately 12 months after birth. When the infant's palm is stroked at the base of the fingers, the fingers close into a firm grasp starting from the pinky finger.

Peripheral Vision: is the eyes' ability to use side vision while gazing straight ahead.

Postural Reflex: are mature patterns of responses that control balance, motor coordination, and sensory motor development.

Sensory Integration: is a term developed by Jean Ayers, which explains how the brain receives, perceives, and reacts to sensory information either from inside or outside the body. She defines sensory integration as *"The neurological process that organizes sensation from one's own body and from the environment and makes it possible to use the body effectively within the environment."*

Spatial Orientation: is the brain's ability to orient self to the ground with or without vision.

Spinal Galant: is a primitive reflex pattern present in the womb and that integrates at approximately 9-12 months of age. When the right or left side of the back below the waist is stroked, the sensation causes the child to side bend towards the touch.

Symmetrical Tonic Neck Reflex (STNR): is a primitive reflex pattern that usually emerges in utero and continues to develop after birth. It becomes active approximately six months of age and starts to integrate at approximately ten months of age. The STNR is an involuntary reaction to downward and upward movement of the head. There are two STNR positions. Position 1 is a downward head movement which causes the elbows to flex and the legs to extend. Position 2 is an upward head movement (also called Sphinx Position) which causes the elbows to extend and the legs to flex.

Tonic Labyrinthine Reflex (TLR): is a primitive reflex pattern that usually emerges in utero and continues to develop after birth. The TLR is an involuntary reaction to the forward and backward movement of the head. There are two types: TLR Forward and TLR Backward. TLR Forward occurs when the head is in front of the spine, causing the arms and legs to flex and tuck inward. TLR Backward occurs when the head is behind the line of the spine, causing the arms and the legs to extend and the back to arch and stiffen.

Vestibular sense: the body's sense of balance and movement

Visual Tracking: is the ability to maintain a visual gaze on a moving object or on a predictable line while reading.

Visual Discrimination: is the ability to recognize details in what is being seen while identifying similarities and differences.

Wilbarger Brushing Protocol: was developed by occupational therapist, Patricia Wilbarger. WBP is a treatment method wherein a child's skin is brushed using a surgical brush in a specific manner throughout the day to desensitize tactile defensiveness.

RESOURCES

Active Baby, Healthy Brain: 135 fun Exercises to Maximize Your Child's Brain Development from Birth through age 5½, by Margaret Sasse.

Assessing Neuromotor Readiness for Learning: The INPP Developmental Screening Test and School Intervention Programme, by Sally Goddard.

Masgutova Neurosensorimotor Reflex Integration programs https://masgutovamethod.com/

Movement That Heals, by Harald Blomberg, MD.

Neuromotor Immaturity in Children and Adults: The INPP Screening Test for Clinicians and Health Practitioners, by Sally Goddard.

Parents' Guide to Masgutova Neurosensorimotor Reflex Integration (MNRI) - by Svetlana Masgutova, PhD. & Denis Masgutova.

Reflexes, Learning and Behavior, by Sally Goddard.

The Misunderstood Child: Understanding and Coping with Your Child's Learning Disabilities, by Larry B. Silver, M.D.

The Out-of-Sync Child: Recognizing and Coping with Sensory Integration Dysfunction, by Carol Stock Kranowitz, M.A.

The Rhythmic Movement Method: A Revolutionary Approach to Improved Health and Well-Being, by Harald Blomberg, MD.

The Symphony of Reflexes: Interventions for Human Development, Autism, CP, and Other Neurological Disorders, by Bonnie L. Brandes Med.

Medical Dictionary: https://medical-dictionary.thefreedictionary.com/

ABOUT THE AUTHOR

Kokeb Girma McDonald is the founder of Polaris Therapy. She has a Bachelor's of Science in Occupational Therapy and Master's of Science in Health Care Administration Management and Change in Health Care Options. Kokeb is a mother of two children with extensive experience working with children from diverse backgrounds. Recognizing the need for effective and universally accessible therapy programs, Kokeb created this guide to empower and reassure frustrated parents and offer fellow professionals a tool to expand their clinical reach.

CAN YOU HELP?

THANK YOU FOR READING MY BOOK!

I really appreciate all of your feedback,
and I love hearing what you have to say.

I need your input to make the next version of this book
and my future books better.

Please leave me an honest review on Amazon letting me know
what you think of the book and how you are using it.

Thanks so much!

Kokeb McDonald, OTR/L
Occupational Therapist Registered/Licensed

Made in the USA
Las Vegas, NV
01 December 2020